Russian Double Bass Album
Russisches Kontrabass-Album

8 Pieces for Double Bass and Piano
8 Stücke für Kontrabass und Klavier

Glière, Koussevitzky, Schillinger, Tchaikovsky

KONTRABASS

F 95087

ROB. FORBERG MUSIKVERLAG

F 95087

ISMN 979-0-2061-0621-7

INDEX · INHALT

Reinhold Moritzevič Glière (1875-1956)

    Tarantella op. 9/2 4

    Scherzo op. 32/2 11

Sergei Aleksandrovich Koussevitzky (1874-1951)

    Two Pieces · Zwei Stücke op. 1

        Andante 15

        Valse miniature 16

    Chanson triste op. 2 18

Joseph Schillinger (1895-1943)

    Scherzino 19

    Poème nocturne 21

Pyotr Ilyich Tchaikovsky (1840-1893)

    Andante cantabile op. 11 22

Tarantella

L'accord

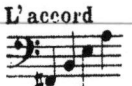

Reinhold Moritzevič Glière (1875-1956)
op. 9/2

Allegro vivace. ♩.= 192.

Meno mosso.

Scherzo

Reinhold Moritzevič Glière
op. 32/2

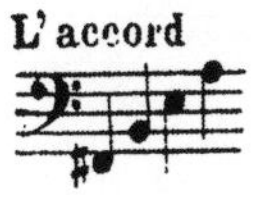

Two Pieces · Zwei Stücke
Andante

Sergei Aleksandrovich Koussevitzky (1874-1951)
op. 1/1

F 95087

KONTRABASS

À Mademoiselle Nathalie Ouchkoff

Valse miniature

Sergei Aleksandrovich Koussevitzky
op. 1/2

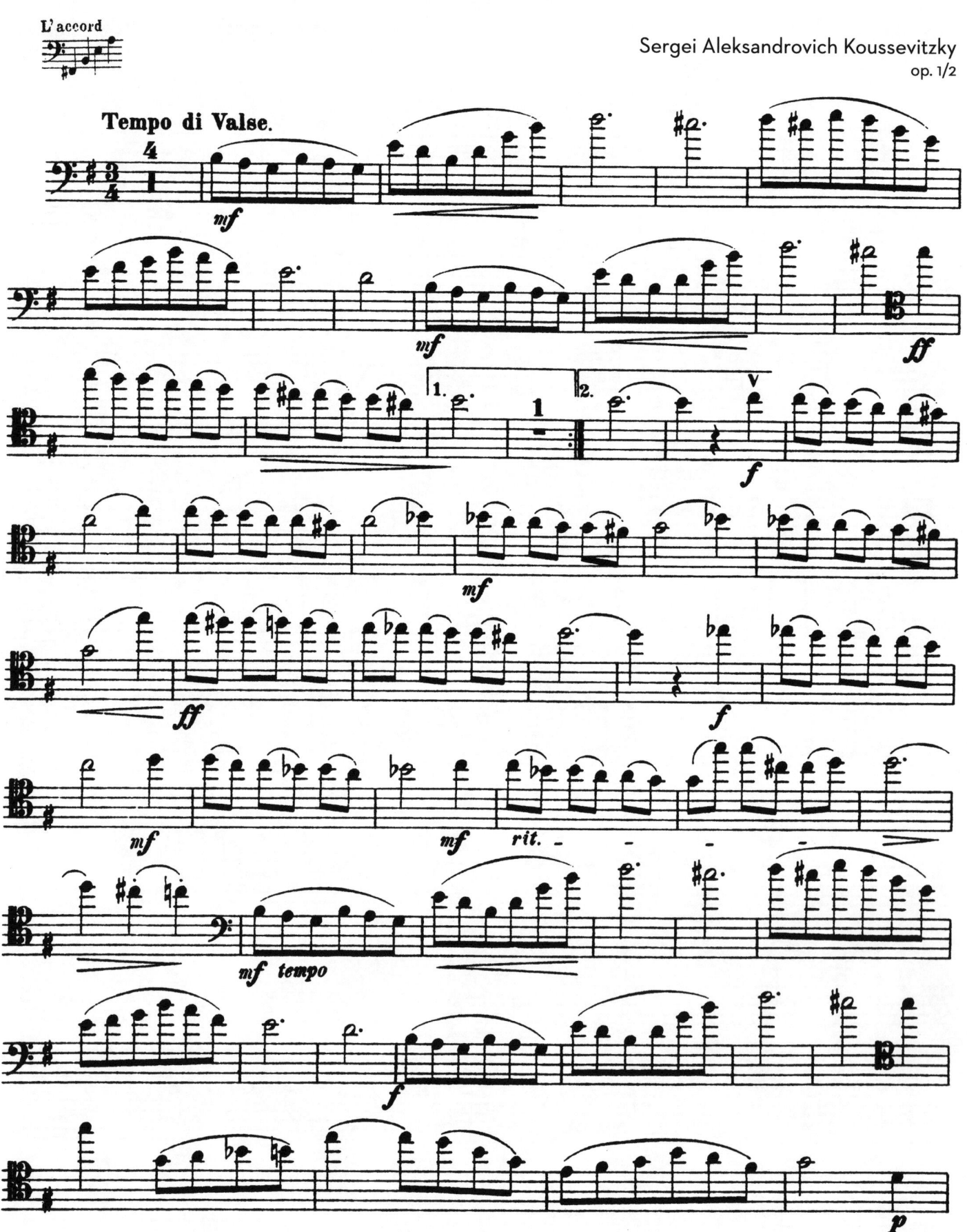

Chanson triste

Sergei Aleksandrovich Koussevitzky
op. 2

Scherzino

Joseph Schillinger (1895-1943)
No. 2 from *Three Pieces* · Nr. 2 aus *Drei Stücke*
Edited by · bearbeitet von Yuri Golubev

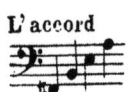

Allegretto

F 95087

Poème nocturne

Joseph Schillinger
No. 3 from *Three Pieces* · Nr. 3 aus *Drei Stücke*
Edited by · bearbeitet von Yuri Golubev

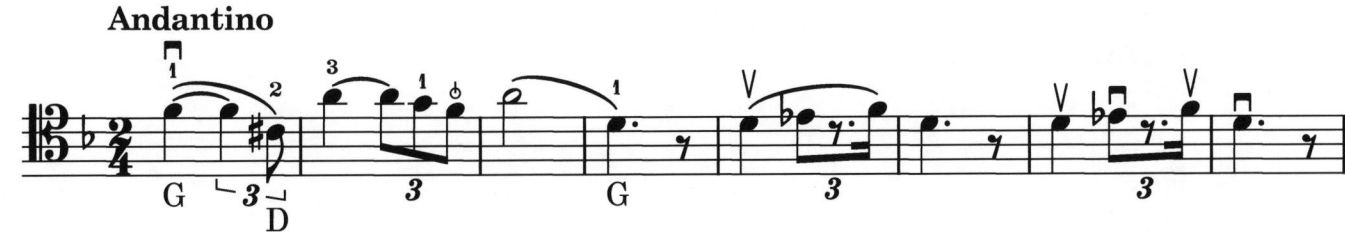

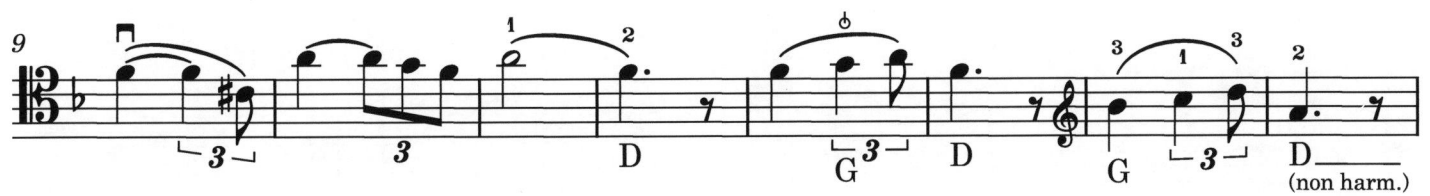

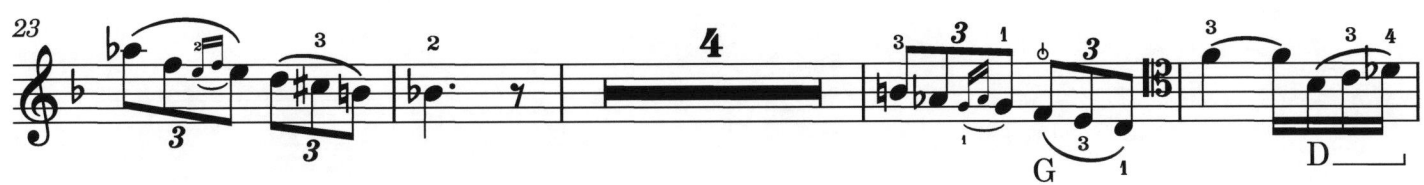

Andante cantabile

Pyotr Ilyich Tchaikovsky (1840-1893)
op. 11
Transcription by · Transkription von Yuri Golubev

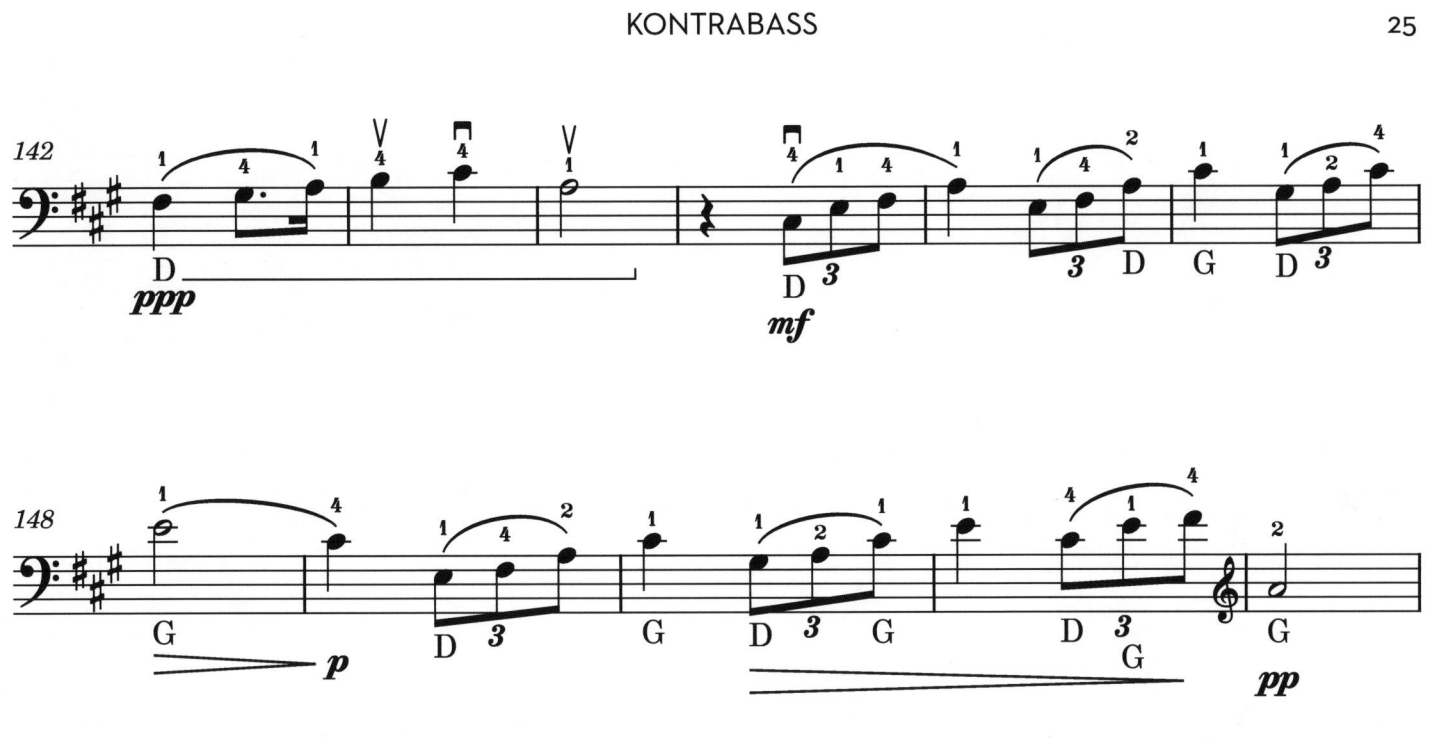

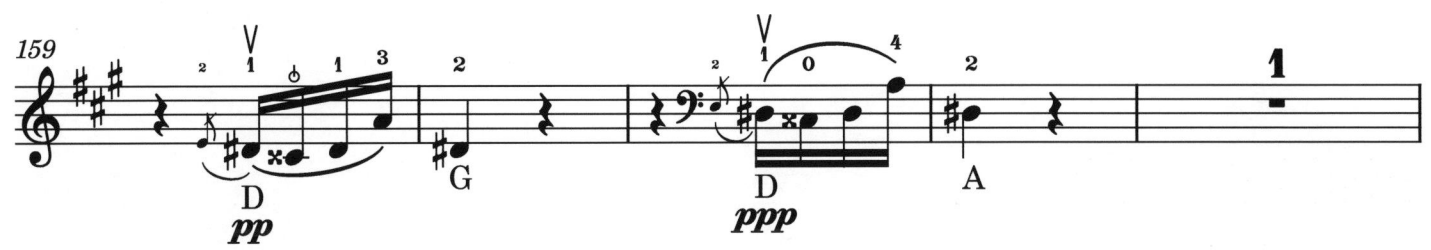

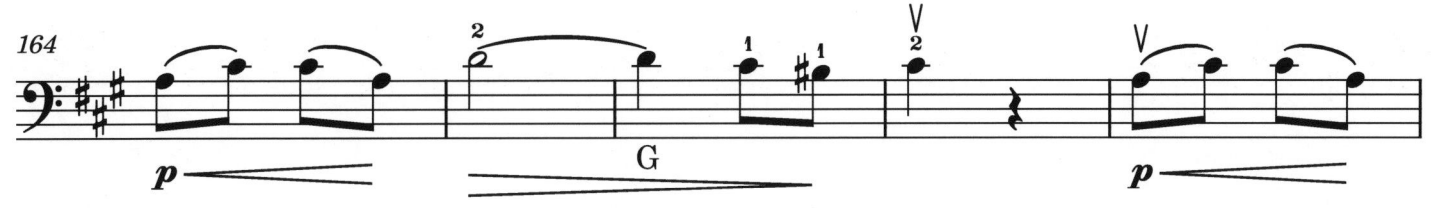

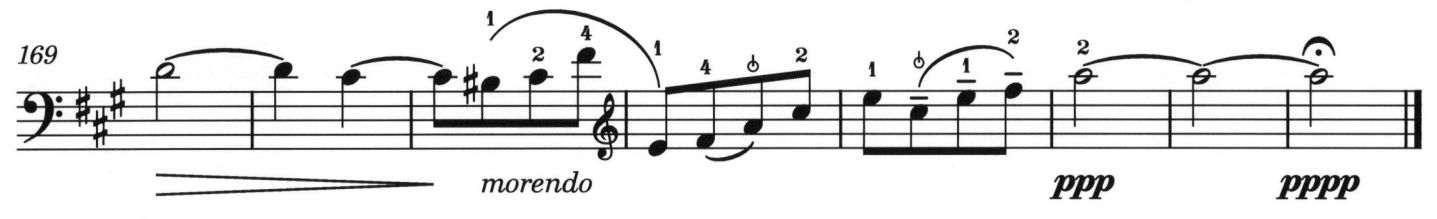